KAISER CHIE S
'Employment'

Published by
Wise Publications,
8/9 Frith Street, London, W1D 3JB, England.

Exclusive distributors:
Music Sales Limited,
Distribution Centre, Newmarket Road, Bury St Edmunds,
Suffolk, IP33 3YB, England.

Music Sales Pty Limited,
120 Rothschild Avenue, Rosebery,
NSW 2018, Australia.

Order No. AM985523
ISBN 1-84609-556-5
This book © Copyright 2006 by Wise Publications,
a division of Music Sales Limited.

Music arrangements by Paul Honey.
Music processed by Paul Ewers Music Design.

Printed in the United Kingdom.

www.musicsales.com

KAISER CHIEFS
'Employment'

WISE PUBLICATIONS
part of The Music Sales Group

London / New York / Paris / Sydney / Copenhagen / Berlin / Madrid / Tokyo

Everyday I Love You Less And Less

Words & Music by Nicholas Hodgson, Richard Wilson,
Andrew White, James Rix & Nicholas Baines

Original key: F#minor

1. Ev - 'ry day I love you less and less, it's

clear to see that you've be-come ob - sessed,
(2.) can't be - lieve once you and me did sex.

I've got to get this mes-sage to the

press,
-dressed,

that ev-'ry day I love you less and less.
since ev-'ry day I love you less and less.

And ev-'ry day I love you less and

less,
less.

I've got to get this feel-ing of my chest,
You're tur-ning in-to some-thing I de-test,

the
and

doc - tor says all I need's pills and rest,
ev - 'ry - bo - dy says that you're a mess,

since ev - 'ry day I love you less and

And my girl-friend loves___ me,

oh!_____

1.

oh!_____

N.C.

2. Ev-'ry day I love you less and less.   I   oh!_____

They keep pho-tos of___ me,   oh!_____

9

That's en-ough love for___ me,___ oh!___

to Coda ⊕

10

Stop! Bleurgh, bleurgh, bleurgh, bleurgh, bleurgh, bleurgh,

bleurgh,_____ bleurgh!_____

D.S. al Coda
w/out repeats

Coda

I Predict A Riot

Words & Music by Nicholas Hodgson, Richard Wilson,
Andrew White, James Rix & Nicholas Baines

1. Oh, watch-ing the peo - ple get
2. Oh, I try to get___ to my

lai - ry is not ve - ry pret - ty, I tell thee.
ta - xi; a man in a track - suit at - tacks me, he

Walk-ing through town___ is quite sca - ry, and not ve - ry sen - si - ble
said that he saw___ it be - fore me, wants to get things___ a bit

ei - ther. A friend of a friend,___ he got beat - en, he
go - ry. Girls run a - round___ with no clothes on to
(%) watch-ing the peo - ple get lai - ry is

looked the wrong way___ at a po - lice - - man; would
bor - row a pound___ for a con - - dom; if it
not ve - ry pret - ty I tell thee.

ne - ver have hap - pened to Smea - - ton, an
was - n't for chip - fat they'd be fro - - zen. They're
Walk - ing through town___ is quite sca - - ry, and

old Le - o - den - si - an.
not ve - ry sen - si - ble. } La,_____
not ve - ry sen - si - ble. }

14

15

ri - ot.

And if there's

an - y - bo - dy left in here, ooh, that does - n't want to be out

there.

Ah,

ah.

1.   **2.**   *D.S. al Coda*

oh,

⊕ Coda   A♭5   D♭   A♭   D♭

there,   I___ pre - dict a   ri - ot.   I___ pre - dict a

1.   **2.**

A♭   D♭   D♭   A♭

ri - ot.   I___ pre - dict a

Modern Way

Words & Music by Nicholas Hodgson, Richard Wilson,
Andrew White, James Rix & Nicholas Baines

1. I know, 'cause I've seen it,___ it was great, and I want it.___
2. Take a___ les-son___ from the ones who have been there.___

There's no___ point in sit-ting,___ go-ing cra-zy___ on my own.
My brain___ is not da-maged,___ but in need of___ some re - pair.

(1.) Do you___ know what___ I was put here___ in the world for?___
(2.) Hold on___ to the bas - ics,___ but we can't change___ all our tac - tics.
3. I know___ where I'm go - ing,___ and that we are___ in the know-ing,___

Could you___ tell me___ ev -'ry word or more?
There's no___ point sit - ting___ go - ing crazy on your own. } It's the
I will___ stop at no - thing___ just to get what I want.

on - ly way___ of get - ing out___ of here.___ It's the

on - ly way___ of get - ting out___ of here.___

19

This is the mo - dern way.

This is the mo - dern way of fak-ing it ev - 'ry day, of tak-ing it as we come.

and tak-ing it as we come. And we're not the on - ly ones.

Is that what we used to say? This is the mo - dern way.

22

Oh My God

Words & Music by Nicholas Hodgson, Richard Wilson,
Andrew White, James Rix & Nicholas Baines

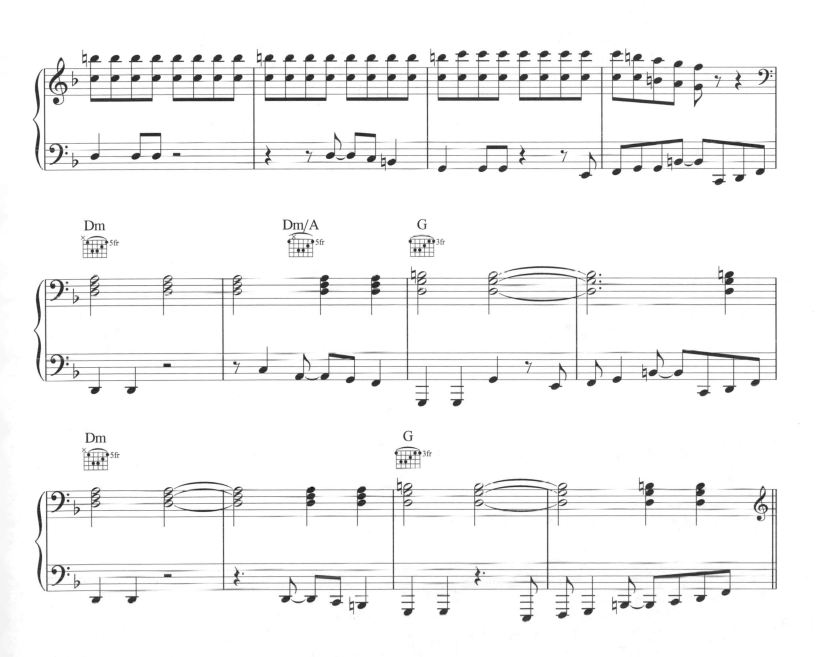

1. Time on your side that will nev - er end, the most beau - ti - ful thing you can
2. Too much time spent drag - ging the past up. I did - n't see you not
3. Great ruins make_ for great - er glo - ries, the on - ly thing grow - ing is

ev - er spend. But you work in a shirt with your name tag on it,
look - ing when I messed up. Set - tl - ing down in your ear - ly twen - ties,
our his - to - ry. Knock me down, I get right back up a - gain,

drift - ing a - part like a plate tec - ton - ic.
sucked more blood than a back - street den - tist. } It don't mat - ter to me_
come back strong - er than a pow - ered up Pac - Man.

'cos all I want-ed to be_____ was a mil - lion miles_ from here

some - where more fa - mil - iar.

Oh, my God, I can't be - lieve_ it, I've nev - er been this far a -

25

26

- way from home.

27

Na Na Na Na Naa

Words & Music by Nicholas Hodgson, Richard Wilson,
Andrew White, James Rix & Nicholas Baines

(Na Na Na Na Naa.   Na Na Na Na Naa.

Na Na Na Na Naa.   Na Na Na Na Naa.)   Oh!

1. It does not move___ me, it does not get me go-ing at all.
2. She does not lis-ten, she's too wrapped up with all of her things.

(Na Na Na Na Naa.   Na Na Na Na Naa.)

It   does   not   shift   me,___   it's
This   does   not   get   to   me 'cause she's

not   the   kind   of   thing   that   I   like.)
not   the   kind   of   girl   that   I   like.)   (Na Na Na Na Naa.

Na Na Na Na Naa.)   Oh!

It does not move___ me, it's not the kind of thing that I like.
She does not move___ me, she's not the kind of girl that I like.

(Na Na Na Na Naa. Na Na Na Na Naa.)

Guitar solo

It does not move___ me, it's not the kind of thing that I like.

(Na Na Na Na Naa.   Na Na Na Na Naa.)

It   does   not   move   me_____   at

It   does   not   move   me,_____   it   does   not   get   me   go - ing   at

all._____

all._____

It   does   not   shift   me_____   I

It   does   not   shift   me,_____   it's   not   the   kind   of   thing   that   I

32

like._____   Oh!
like._____

It   does   not   move_____ me,   it's   not   the   kind   of

thing   that   I   like.   (Na Na Na Na Naa.

Na Na Na Na Naa.)

33

You Can Have It All

Words & Music by Nicholas Hodgson, Richard Wilson,
Andrew White, James Rix & Nicholas Baines

Lead synth

1. I tell you what it's go-ing to be like. I saw you on the bus and that was
2. I tell you what it's go-ing to feel like. You've lost a limb and you can feel it itch you

give it all to you,_____ if it's al - right,_____ oh,___ oh,___ oh.___

Guitar solo

La la la la la la la la la   la la la la la la la la la

if it's al - right,_____ oh,_____ oh.____ oh.____

synth

Born To Be A Dancer

Words & Music by Nicholas Hodgson, Richard Wilson,
Andrew White, James Rix & Nicholas Baines

Dm | Dm/C | B♭

1. You and me we're made (it's im-pos-si-ble to say) to be to-
2. I came down at your (on the Na-tion-al Ex-press) re-quest, to

B♭add9/C | Dm | Dm/C

-ge-ther al-ways. Then you moved a-way (to the ca-pi-tal of
touch your breasts. And there I found that you, you were hang-ing with a

B♭ | B♭add9/C | G | F

En-g-land), I hope you'd stay there. Once you asked me what I'm_ think-ing,
crowd, a load of cheats and li-ars. Do you know what I've been_ think-ing?

Ah.

Ah.

Once you asked me what I'm think - ing, I lay back and think of___ Eng - land. Do you know my re - al___ ans - wer?

Saturday Night

Words & Music by Nicholas Hodgson, Richard Wilson,
Andrew White, James Rix & Nicholas Baines

try and throw this par - ty just as far as you can.___

C - c - c -

-cre - o - sote is pour-ing out of my brain, I swear__ I heard the floor - boards, they were
-pneu - mo - thorax is a word__ that is long. They're just trying to put some punk back in - to

creak-ing your name. G -g -g -get a room, get a head,__ get a hat.__ We're
punc - tured__ lung. P -p -p -pa - nic over, par - ty off, __ par - ty on 'cause we are

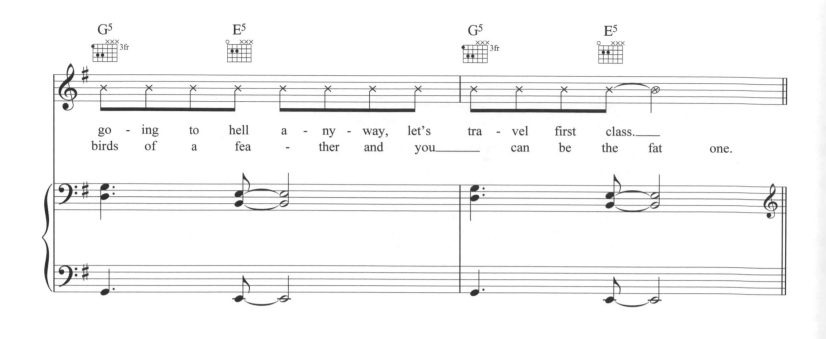

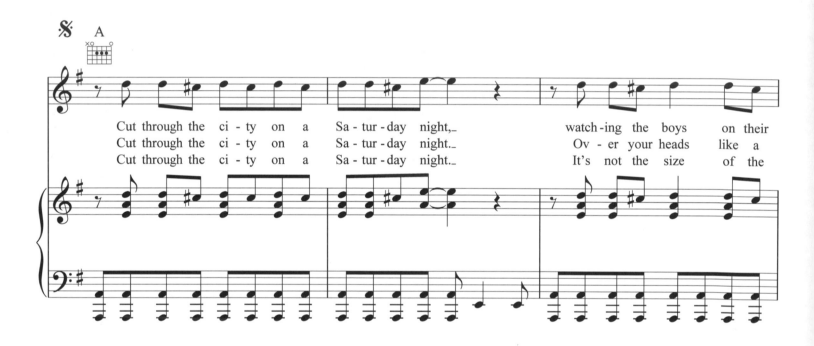

50

thir - ty,___ I want to do it on your birth - day.___

D⁵

'Cause I don't want to waste a mo-ment with you,___ I just want to dance the

E⁵

whole night through.___ Cut through the ci - ty on a Sa - tur - day night,___ 'cause

A⁵

you and me,___ we're on the edge of a knife.___

What Did I Ever Give You?

Words & Music by Nicholas Hodgson, Richard Wilson,
Andrew White, James Rix & Nicholas Baines

1. Head down, keep your head down, keep the rent down, o - ver time.

Hold tight to your Red Stripe. Why do

we fight ev-'ry time? I wish that you could see me in the

day, I hope that you'll re-mem-ber me that way.

2. Night - club, Marl- boro Light stub stuck to my gob all the
3. Dis - graced, back to my place. I'm a com-plete waste of your

time.
time. I treat you like you're see-through, I don't
I'm a-sleep be-fore the first sheep, un-til the

54

mean to   ev - 'ry time.
last bleep   of all time.   I   wish that you could see me in the

day,   I hope that you'll re-mem-ber me that way.   What did I ev - er give

you when you want-ed me____ to? All I gave you was____ pain, and a look of dis -

-dain. What did I ev - er give you when you want-ed me____ to? All I gave you was____

grief, are you sick to your___ teeth? Ah,_____ oh,___

oh,___ oh,___ oh.___

57

Time Honoured Tradition

Words & Music by Nicholas Hodgson, Richard Wilson,
Andrew White, James Rix & Nicholas Baines

1. Well it's a time ho-noured tra-di-tion to get e-nough nu-tri-tion.
   not an old wive's tale,___ too much red meat and ale___ will

Stay a-live un-til you die and that is the end of you. And
make you pay, get five a day or that is the end of you. And it's a

I pi-ty the fools___ who don't re-cog-nise the rules.___ You
com-mon mis-con-cep-tion, but true, with-out ex-cep-tion. These

can - not cheat the reap-er's reap, and that is the end of that, that is the end of
nights of booze catch up with you's and that is an ac - tual fact. That is the end of

that, that is the end of that, that is the end of that.
that, that is the end of that, that is the end of that.

Oh oh___ oh oh___ oh oh___ oh oh___ oh oh oh___

oh oh___ oh oh___ oh oh___ 2. It's oh oh___

1. **2.**

La la la___ la la la la___ la la la la la la la la___

la la la___ la la la la___ la la la la la la la la.___

Guitar solo

Oh oh___ oh oh___ oh oh___ oh oh___ oh

oh oh___ oh oh___ oh oh___ oh oh___

La la la___ la la la la___ la la la la la la la la___

la la la___ la la la la___ la la la la la la la.___ Well it's a

time ho - noured tra - di - tion to get e - nough nu - tri - tion.

Stay a - live un - til you die and that is the end of you. And

I pi - ty the fools___ who don't re - cog - nise the rules.___ We

molto rall.

can - not cheat the reap - er's reap, and that is the end of that.

Caroline, Yes

Words & Music by Nicholas Hodgson, Richard Wilson,
Andrew White, James Rix & Nicholas Baines

you are ev -'ry-thing I want to be._____

2. Well you got ev -'ry-thing so why, oh why, did you have to take
3. Well you go your way and____ I'll go mine. But my way's bet - er and it

Ca - ro - line? I bet you thought that was the death of me, 'cause
took less time. Peo - ple say now that you look like me, 'cause

you are ev -'ry-thing I want to be._____
you are ev -'ry-thing I want to be._____

In my

Team Mate

Words & Music by Nicholas Hodgson, Richard Wilson,
Andrew White, James Rix & Nicholas Baines

1. We used to go___ out night - ly___ to the ar - mour - y.
2. We used to hold___ on tight - ly, ___ and you re - lied___ on me.

me and you on a bi - cy - cle for two,
me and you on a bi - cy - cle for two.

aah.
aah,
aah.
Aah.
aah.
Aah.

123456789

KAISER CHIEFS
'Employment'